SHORT
AND SIMPLE

SHORT AND SIMPLE

Music for the

- Processional

- Gospel Fanfare

- Offertory

- Communion

- Recessional

with or without pedals

Colin Mawby

kevin
mayhew

We hope you enjoy *Short and Simple*.
Further copies of this and our many other books are available
from your local Kevin Mayhew stockist.

In case of difficulty, or to request a catalogue,
please contact the publisher direct by writing to:

The Sales Department
KEVIN MAYHEW LTD
Buxhall
Stowmarket
Suffolk IP14 3BW

Phone 01449 737978
Fax 01449 737834
E-mail info@kevinmayhewltd.com

First published in Great Britain in 2002 by Kevin Mayhew Ltd.

© Copyright 2002 Kevin Mayhew Ltd.

ISBN 1 84003 935 3
ISMN M 57024 098 2
Catalogue No: 1400329

0 1 2 3 4 5 6 7 8 9

Cover design: Angela Selfe
Music setter: Donald Thomson
Proof reader: Tracy Cook

Printed and bound in Great Britain

Contents

PROCESSIONAL

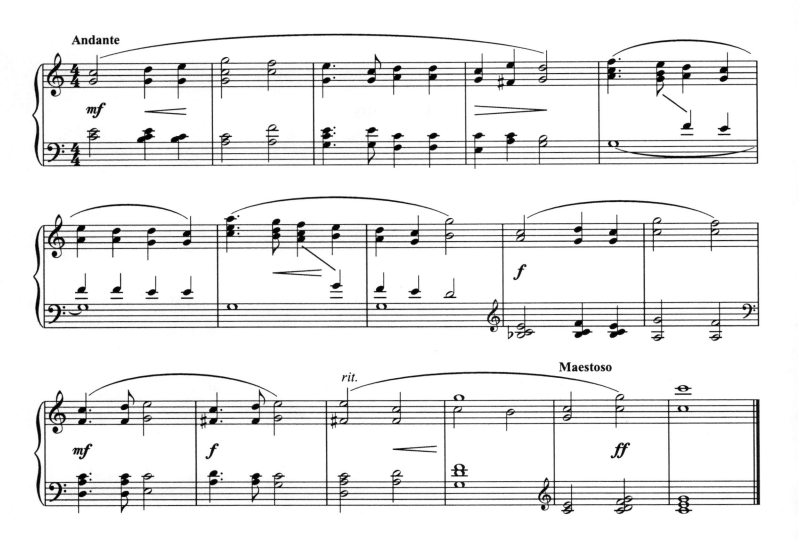

PROCESSIONAL

PROCESSIONAL

FANFARE FOR THE GOSPEL

FANFARE FOR THE GOSPEL

FANFARE FOR THE GOSPEL

OFFERTORY

OFFERTORY

OFFERTORY

COMMUNION

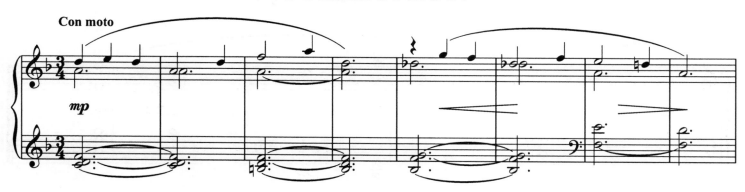

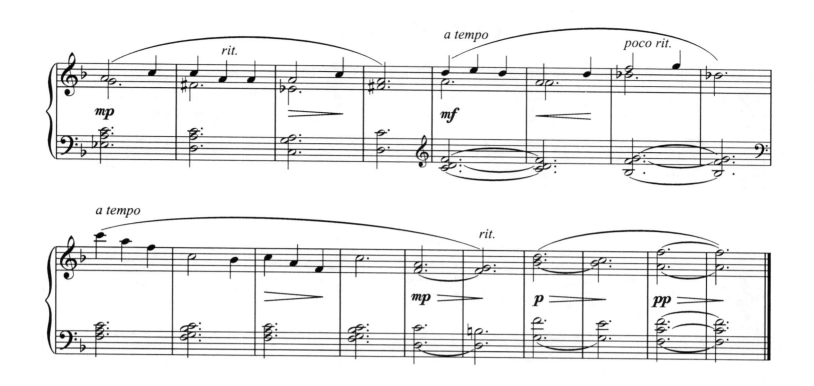

COMMUNION

COMMUNION

RECESSIONAL

RECESSIONAL

RECESSIONAL